WeightWatchers®

KT-433-169

HEARTY HOME
cooking

SIMON & SCHUSTER
A CBS COMPANY

Sue Ashworth

First published in Great Britain by
Simon & Schuster UK Ltd, 2010.
A CBS Company

SIMON AND SCHUSTER
ILLUSTRATED BOOKS
Simon & Schuster UK Ltd
222 Gray's Inn Road
London WC1X 8HB

Weight Watchers Publications Team: Jane Griffiths,
Donna Watts, Tori Rozputynski and Nina McKerlie
Simon & Schuster Project Editor: Anna Hitchin
Photography by Steve Baxter
Prop styling by Kim Morphew
Food preparation by Sue Ashworth
Design and typesetting by Jane Humphrey

Printed and bound in Singapore
Colour reproduction by Dot Gradations Ltd, UK
A CIP catalogue for this book is available from
the British Library

Pictured on the front cover: Toad in the Hole, page 33

*Pictured on the back cover from top to bottom and left to
right:* Carrot Cake Muffins, page 12; Chunky Butter Bean
Soup, page 17; Filo Turkey Pie, page 31; Pancakes with
Chocolate Sauce, page 53

Pictured on the contents page:
Baked Fish and Spicy Chips, page 34

Pictured on page 4: Apricot Bread and
Butter Pudding, page 58

ProPoints® value logo: You'll find this easy
to read **ProPoints** value logo on every recipe
throughout this book. The logo represents the number
of **ProPoints** values per serving each recipe contains.
It is not an indication of the fillingness of a recipe.

Weight Watchers **ProPoints** Weight Loss System is
a simple way to lose weight. As part of the Weight
Watchers **ProPoints** plan you'll enjoy eating delicious,
healthy, filling foods that help to keep you feeling
satisfied for longer and in control of your portions.

Filling & Healthy Foods are highlighted in green.
Focus on these foods where you can – they are healthy
choices that will help you to feel satisfied for longer.

Ⓥ This symbol denotes a vegetarian recipe and
assumes that, where relevant, free range eggs,
vegetarian cheese, vegetarian virtually fat free fromage
frais, vegetarian low fat crème fraîche and vegetarian
low fat yogurts are used. Virtually fat free fromage frais,
low fat crème fraîche and low fat yogurts may contain
traces of gelatine so they are not always vegetarian.
Please check the labels.

❄ This symbol denotes a dish that can be frozen.

Recipe notes

Egg size Medium, unless otherwise stated.

All fruits and vegetables Medium size unless
otherwise stated.

Raw eggs Only the freshest eggs should be used.
Pregnant women, the elderly and children should avoid
recipes with eggs which are not fully cooked or raw.

Recipe timings These are approximate and meant to
be guidelines. Please note that the preparation time
includes all the steps up to and following the main
cooking time(s).

Low fat spread Where a recipe states to use a low fat
spread, a light spread with a fat content of no less than
38% should be used.

Stock Stock cubes should be used, unless otherwise
stated. Prepare according to the packet instructions.

contents

Introduction **4**

Wake up call **6**

Lunch break **16**

Traditional suppers **30**

Modern suppers **40**

What's for pudding? **52**

Index by *ProPoints* values **62**

Index **63**

ideas for all
the family...

Hearty Home Cooking is the exciting new cookbook from Weight Watchers, developed to work alongside the **ProPoints plan**. You'll be delighted by this delicious selection of 60 new recipes, covering some of the best of traditional and modern British cooking – and they're all prepared with a minimum of fuss.

The recipes have clear step-by-step instructions enabling both new and experienced cooks to discover fabulous everyday dishes. You'll find everything from breakfasts and lunches to suppers and desserts. Many of the recipes in *Hearty Home Cooking* contain **Filling & Healthy Foods** which can help you to stay satisfied for longer. The **ProPoints** values are also clearly shown on every recipe, calculated using its protein, carbohydrate, fat and fibre content.

The **ProPoints** system is a unique and totally flexible way to lose weight. It can easily be adapted to suit the different demands of your life, whether you're juggling work and family, managing on a budget, based at home or often away travelling. With the **ProPoints plan**, you can still eat the foods you enjoy and lose weight at a healthy, sustainable rate.

Enjoy the pleasures of cooking with these delicious recipes and add to your list of family favourites.

wake up call

Get a great start to the day with these delicious breakfasts. Easy to make and filling too, they'll set you up and keep you satisfied. On a busy weekday, heat up some Porridge with Mango and Pineapple or enjoy Eggy Bread with Bananas. And when the weekend arrives, chill out with Rosti with Sausages and Eggs.

Spiced fruits with cinnamon toast

[5 ProPoints value]

On a chilly morning, it's a pleasure to wake up to this warm and spicy fruit salad.

Ⓥ **Serves 4** ● **Takes 15** minutes ● **20** *ProPoints* values per recipe

> 1 eating apple, cored and sliced
> 4 plums, pitted and sliced
> 200 ml (7 fl oz) orange juice
> 15 g (½ oz) light muscovado or caster sugar
> ¼ teaspoon ground mixed spice
> 75 g (2¾ oz) ready to eat, semi-dried apricots, halved
> 25 g (1 oz) sultanas or raisins
> 1 large orange
> 4 medium slices white or brown bread
> a little ground cinnamon, for sprinkling
> 4 tablespoons low fat plain yogurt, to serve

Method

1 Put the apple and plums in a saucepan with the orange juice and 3 tablespoons of water. Add the sugar, mixed spice, apricots and sultanas or raisins. Cook gently for about 6–8 minutes until the apple and plums are tender.

2 Meanwhile, use a sharp serrated knife to remove all the peel and pith from the orange. Slice the flesh into segments, removing all the membrane. Add the segments to the saucepan. Stir gently to mix them in, then share the fruit between four serving dishes.

3 Sprinkle the bread slices with a little cinnamon, then toast them lightly under a grill. Top each portion of fruit with 1 tablespoon of yogurt and then serve with the cinnamon toast.

Try this... Slice in 1 banana before adding the yogurt in step 3, for no extra *ProPoints* values per serving.

Tip... The fruit salad will keep for up to four days in the fridge.

Porridge with mango and pineapple

6 ProPoints value

This simple recipe tastes fantastic, looks great and is an excellent way to start the day.

Ⓥ **Serves 2** ● **Takes 10** minutes ● **12 ProPoints** values per recipe

- 75 g (2¾ oz) **porridge oats** with wheatbran
- 15 g (½ oz) dried cranberries
- 15 g (½ oz) sultanas
- 15 g (½ oz) ready to eat, semi-dried apricots, chopped
- 2 tablespoons **0% fat Greek yogurt**
- 50 g (1¾ oz) fresh **mango**, peeled, stoned and chopped
- 1 canned **pineapple ring in natural juice**, drained and chopped

Method

1 Put the porridge oats in a non stick saucepan with 350 ml (12 fl oz) water, the cranberries, sultanas and apricots. Bring to the boil, stirring, then reduce the heat and cook gently for 3–4 minutes, stirring constantly.

2 Share the porridge between two bowls and spoon 1 tablespoon of yogurt on top of each. Share the mango and pineapple between the bowls. Serve at once.

Ⓥ **Try this...** As an alternative topping, use 100 g (3½ oz) thawed frozen **raspberries** instead of the **pineapple** and **mango** for the same **ProPoints** values per serving.

Ⓥ **Or this...** Instead of mango, use two canned **pineapple rings in natural juice** for the same **ProPoints** values per serving.

Eggy bread with bananas

4 ProPoints value

Ⓥ **Serves 2** ● **Takes 10** minutes ● **9 ProPoints** values per recipe

- 2 medium slices white bread, crusts removed
- 1 **egg**
- 5 tablespoons **skimmed milk**
- ½ teaspoon vanilla extract
- low fat cooking spray
- 2 teaspoons golden syrup
- 2 small **bananas**, sliced

Method

1 Cut each slice of bread in half diagonally.

2 In a large and shallow dish, beat together the egg, milk and vanilla extract. Add the bread slices and leave them to soak for 5 minutes, turning them over once so each side gets a good soaking.

3 Heat a large non stick frying pan and spray with the cooking spray. Add the soaked bread and cook it gently for about 1–2 minutes until it has set and turned golden brown. Turn over and cook on the other side for another 1–2 minutes.

4 Share the bread between two warm serving plates. Add the syrup and the bananas to the frying pan. Heat and bubble up the mixture for about 30 seconds, then spoon over the bread and serve immediately.

Ⓥ **Try this...** Instead of bananas, you can use 200 g (7 oz) **mixed berries** (either fresh or thawed frozen ones) for the same **ProPoints** values per serving.

Tip... Slightly stale bread is ideal for this recipe so it's a good way to use up a two or three day old loaf. Since it is drier than fresh bread, it soaks up more liquid.

Scotch pancakes with turkey rashers

Relax and unwind on the weekend with a pancake breakfast.

Serves 4 ● Takes 20 minutes ● **17** *ProPoints* values per recipe

- 75 g (2¾ oz) plain flour
- a pinch of salt
- 1 teaspoon baking powder
- 1 egg
- 3 tablespoons low fat plain yogurt
- 1 tablespoon skimmed milk
- 4 tomatoes, halved
- 8 turkey rashers
- ½ teaspoon vegetable oil
- freshly ground black pepper

Method

1 Preheat the grill. Sift the flour, salt and baking powder into a mixing bowl. Add the egg, yogurt and milk, then use a hand whisk to beat the ingredients together to make a smooth batter.

2 Arrange the tomatoes on the grill rack. Grill for 5 minutes then arrange the turkey rashers beside them and grill for 2 minutes.

3 Meanwhile, cook the pancakes. Heat a non stick frying pan until hot and then add the vegetable oil. Add tablespoonfuls of the batter mixture and cook over a medium low heat, turning them over when bubbles start to appear on the surface. Each pancake takes about 2 minutes to cook and at least four should fit into the pan.

4 Serve two pancakes, two turkey rashers and two tomato halves per person, seasoned with some black pepper.

Tip... You can make the batter a couple of hours in advance, if you like. Simply keep it covered and chilled, then stir well before cooking.

Courgette and chorizo frittata

A deliciously satisfying breakfast.

Serves 4 ● Takes 15 minutes to prepare,
20 minutes to cook ● 18 *ProPoints* values per recipe

  50 g (1¾ oz) chorizo sausage, chopped
  1 large courgette, grated
  6 eggs, beaten
  4 tablespoons skimmed milk
  40 g (1½ oz) half fat mature Cheddar
    cheese, grated
  salt and freshly ground black pepper

Method

1 Preheat the oven to Gas Mark 6/200°C/fan oven
180°C.
2 Put the chorizo in a medium size, non stick
frying pan. Heat on the hob and cook gently over
a medium heat for 2–3 minutes, until the fat begins
to run. Add the courgette and cook, stirring, for
a further 2–3 minutes. Remove from the heat and
transfer to a 23 cm (9 inch) round baking dish.
3 In a bowl, beat together the eggs and milk.
Season, then pour into the baking dish and sprinkle
with the grated cheese. Transfer to the oven and
bake for 15–20 minutes until set and golden. Cool
slightly then cut into four equal pieces and serve.

Ⓥ Try this... For a vegetarian frittata, omit the
chorizo and cook the courgette in a little low fat
cooking spray before adding the eggs and cheese.
The *ProPoints* values per serving will be 4.

Tip... If you have an ovenproof frying pan, you
could cook the chorizo and courgette first, then
add the rest of the ingredients before transferring
to the oven.

Strawberry muesli smoothie

[5 ProPoints value]

This smoothie's delicious strawberry flavour will wake you up in the morning.

Ⓥ Serves 1 ● Takes 5 minutes + overnight soaking ● **5 ProPoints** values per recipe

20 g (¾ oz) low sugar fruit muesli
4 tablespoons unsweetened apple juice
100 g (3½ oz) low fat strawberry yogurt
100 g (3½ oz) strawberries, halved

Method

1 The night before, put the muesli in a large jug and add the apple juice, stirring to mix. Cover and leave overnight to soak. If you prefer, soak the muesli in the morning for 15–20 minutes.
2 Add the remaining ingredients to the jug, then use a hand held blender to blend the mixture until smooth. Alternatively, transfer the mixture to a smoothie maker or blender and blend until smooth.
3 Pour into a glass and serve at once.

Ⓥ Try this... Use low fat raspberry yogurt instead of strawberry yogurt and use 100 g (3½ oz) fresh or frozen **raspberries** instead of **strawberries**. There's no need to thaw the raspberries first – they'll just blend in to make the smoothie super chilled. The **ProPoints** values per serving will remain the same.

> *Cook's ideas...*
> **If a busy schedule might interfere with breakfast,** prepare ahead, then grab a smoothie or muffin in the morning.

Carrot cake muffins

[5 ProPoints value]

Ⓥ ❄ Makes 10 ● Takes 15 minutes to prepare + cooling, **30** minutes to bake ● **48 ProPoints** values per recipe

200 g (7 oz) plain flour
2 teaspoons baking powder
100 g (3½ oz) light muscovado sugar
1 egg
1 teaspoon vanilla extract
100 ml (3½ fl oz) skimmed milk
50 g (1¾ oz) low fat spread, melted
250 g (9 oz) carrots, peeled and grated finely
50 g (1¾ oz) raisins

For the icing
125 g (4½ oz) low fat soft cheese
1 tablespoon light muscovado sugar
2 teaspoons finely grated orange zest, reserving
  1 teaspoon for decoration

Method

1 Preheat the oven to Gas Mark 6/200°C/fan oven 180°C. Place 10 paper muffin cases in a muffin tray, or line the tray with individual squares of greaseproof paper instead.
2 Sift the flour and baking powder into a mixing bowl, then stir in the sugar.
3 In a jug, beat together the egg, vanilla extract, milk and melted spread. Add to the dry ingredients with the grated carrots and raisins. Stir until just combined. For the best results, don't over-mix.
4 Spoon the mixture into the paper cases and transfer to the oven. Bake for 25–30 minutes until risen and golden. Cool on a wire rack.
5 To make the topping, mix together the soft cheese, sugar and orange zest, allowing a couple of minutes for the sugar to dissolve. Swirl an equal amount on to each muffin, sprinkle with the reserved zest and serve.

Ⓥ Try this... Enjoy a muffin on the go, without the icing, for 4 **ProPoints** values per muffin.

Creamy mushrooms on toast

[5 ProPoints value]

These tasty mushrooms are also perfect for a light lunch.

Serves 1 ● **Takes 10** minutes ● **5 ProPoints** values per recipe

> 150 g (5½ oz) mushrooms, sliced
> 150 ml (5 fl oz) skimmed milk
> 2 teaspoons cornflour
> 1 thick slice wholemeal bread
> salt and freshly ground black pepper

Method

1 Put the mushrooms in a non stick saucepan with the milk and season. Bring up to the boil, then reduce the heat and simmer for 5 minutes. Take care that the milk does not boil over.
2 Blend the cornflour with 1 tablespoon of cold water and then add it to the mushrooms. Heat, stirring until thickened, then cook gently for a few more seconds.
3 Meanwhile, toast the bread. Pile the mushroom mixture on top of the toast and serve immediately.

Try this... For a simple supper, instead of the bread, enjoy the mushroom mixture with 40 g (1½ oz) dried pasta or 40 g (1½ oz) dried brown rice, cooked according to the packet instructions, for a total **ProPoints** value of 7.

Rosti with sausages and eggs

[6 ProPoints value]

Enjoy a grilled tomato or some mushrooms cooked in stock on the side, for no additional **ProPoints** values.

Serves 2 ● **Takes 15** minutes to prepare + cooling, **35** minutes to cook ● **12 ProPoints** values per recipe

> 200 g (7 oz) potatoes, peeled
> low fat cooking spray
> 2 eggs, beaten
> 2 low fat sausages
> 2 tablespoons skimmed milk
> salt and freshly ground black pepper

Method

1 Put the potatoes in a saucepan, cover with water and bring to the boil. Cook for 10 minutes. Drain, cover with cold water and leave to cool.
2 Preheat the oven to Gas Mark 6/200°C/fan oven 180°C. Spray a non stick baking tray with the cooking spray.
3 Drain the cooled potatoes and coarsely grate into a mixing bowl and season. Add 2 tablespoons of the beaten egg and stir lightly to mix. Place four equal amounts on the baking sheet, flattening them to make even rounds. Place the sausages beside them.
4 Bake in the oven for 25 minutes, turning over the rosti and sausages after 15 minutes.
5 When almost ready, make the scrambled eggs. Beat the milk into the remaining eggs. Heat a non stick saucepan and spray with the cooking spray. Add the eggs and cook over a medium heat, stirring with a wooden spoon, until set and scrambled. Share the egg between two warmed plates and serve with two rosti and one sausage per person.

Smoked fish ramekins

You can serve these ramekins cold as a spread and they're ideal as a packed lunch too.

Serves 6 ● **Takes 15** minutes to prepare,
20 minutes to cook ● **34** *ProPoints* values per recipe

low fat cooking spray
250 g (9 oz) skinned, boneless smoked
   haddock fillet, *cut into chunks*
75 g (2¾ oz) *smoked salmon, snipped into*
   tiny pieces
100 g (3½ oz) *low fat soft cheese*
4 eggs, *beaten*
200 ml (7 fl oz) skimmed milk
1 *tablespoon chopped* fresh chives, parsley
   or spring onions
6 *medium slices wholemeal bread*
freshly ground black pepper

Method

1 Preheat the oven to Gas Mark 4/180°C/fan oven 160°C. Spray six ramekin dishes or individual baking dishes with the cooking spray.

2 Mix together the haddock and salmon then share the mixture between the prepared dishes. Place the dishes on a baking tray.

3 Tip the soft cheese into a bowl and beat with a wooden spoon to soften it. Whisk in the eggs and milk to make a smooth mixture, then stir in the chives, parsley or spring onions. Season with a little black pepper; you won't need any salt. Pour an equal amount of the mixture into each dish.

4 Bake in the oven for 15–20 minutes until set. Leave to cool for a few minutes. Meanwhile, toast the bread and cut in half. Serve with the fish.

lunch break

Discover inspiring new ideas for lunch.

No matter how busy you are, at home or on the go, make time to savour delicious **soups and sandwiches, salads and gratins**; relax with recipes such as Curried Chicken Soup or Leek and Ham Gratins, and enjoy fabulous, satisfying flavours.

Chunky butter bean soup

4 ProPoints value

Quick and tasty, this soup is so satisfying.

Ⓥ ❄ **Serves 4** ● **Takes 10** minutes to prepare, **35** minutes to cook ● **17** *ProPoints* values per recipe

300 g (10½ oz) swede or turnip, peeled and chopped
2 carrots, peeled and chopped
1 onion, chopped
1.2 litres (2 pints) vegetable stock
1 teaspoon celery seeds
2 x 410 g cans butter beans, drained
150 g (5½ oz) canned sweetcorn, drained or frozen sweetcorn, thawed
2 tablespoons roughly chopped fresh parsley
freshly ground black pepper

Method

1 Put the swede or turnip, carrots, onion, stock and celery seeds into a large lidded saucepan. Bring to the boil. Cover, reduce the heat and simmer for 20 minutes or until the vegetables are tender.
2 Add the butter beans and sweetcorn to the saucepan. Cover and cook over a low heat for a further 15 minutes.
3 Using a hand held blender, partially blend the soup to give it more body. Alternatively, tip half of the soup into a blender or liquidiser, blend until smooth, and then return it to the saucepan with the rest of the soup.
4 Add the parsley, reheat, then season with black pepper. Ladle into bowls and serve at once.

Ⓥ **Try this...** If you prefer, use two cans of mixed beans in water instead of butter beans, for no extra *ProPoints* values per serving. For a spicier soup, use cumin seeds instead of celery seeds.

Pasta with peppers and courgettes

6 ProPoints value

Ⓥ ❄ **Serves 4** ● **Takes 25** minutes ● **25** *ProPoints* values per recipe

> 100 g (3½ oz) dried pasta shapes
> low fat cooking spray
> 1 red **pepper**, de-seeded and chopped
> 1 small **courgette**, grated
> 100 g (3½ oz) canned or frozen **sweetcorn**
> 4 **eggs**
> 2 tablespoons **skimmed milk**
> 50 g (1¾ oz) half fat mature Cheddar cheese, grated
> 2 teaspoons dried mixed herbs
> salt and freshly ground black pepper

Method

1 Bring a pan of water to the boil, add the pasta and cook until just tender or according to the packet instructions. Rinse with cold water to cool the pasta quickly, then drain thoroughly.

2 Meanwhile, heat a non stick frying pan until hot and spray with the cooking spray. Add the pepper and cook over a medium heat for 3–4 minutes, stirring often. Remove from the heat and add the courgette, sweetcorn and pasta, mixing well.

3 Beat the eggs and milk together, then stir in the cheese and herbs. Season and pour into the frying pan with the pasta and vegetables. Cook over a low heat for 4–5 minutes, without stirring, to set the base. Meanwhile, preheat the grill to medium high.

4 Put the frying pan under the grill and cook for 4–5 minutes until the surface has set and is golden brown. Serve at once, or cool completely if serving for a packed lunch. Cut into wedges and wrap in cling film or greaseproof paper. Chill until needed.

Ⓥ **Try this...** Instead of pasta, you could use 225 g (8 oz) cooked **potatoes**, chopped into chunks. The *ProPoints* values per serving will be 5.

Crunchy coleslaw with pine nut kernels

3 ProPoints value

A much lighter but equally tasty version of traditional coleslaw.

Ⓥ **Serves 4** ● **Takes 20** minutes ● **13** *ProPoints* values per recipe

> 150 g (5½ oz) low fat soft cheese
> 100 g (3½ oz) **low fat plain yogurt**
> ¼ small **white cabbage**, shredded finely
> ¼ small **red cabbage**, shredded finely
> 1 small red **onion**, sliced thinly
> 1 **carrot**, peeled and grated
> 1 eating **apple**, unpeeled, cored and chopped
> 25 g (1 oz) raisins or sultanas
> 25 g (1 oz) pine nut kernels
> salt and freshly ground black pepper

Method

1 To make the dressing, put the soft cheese into a large bowl and beat it with a hand whisk or wooden spoon to make it soft and creamy. Add the yogurt, stirring it in until smooth.

2 Add the white and red cabbage, onion, carrot, apple and raisins or sultanas to the bowl. Toss them in the dressing.

3 To toast the pine nut kernels, put them in a dry frying pan and cook them gently over a medium heat for a couple of minutes until lightly browned. Season the coleslaw then serve sprinkled with the toasted pine nut kernels.

Ⓥ **Try this...** You can add 160 g (5¾ oz) half fat Cheddar cheese cubes to the coleslaw for a total of 6 *ProPoints* values per serving.

Tip... If you plan to keep the coleslaw for a day or two, you could use 50 g (1¾ oz) seedless red or green **grapes** instead of the **apple**, which tends to go brown after a while. Make sure you keep the coleslaw covered and refrigerated. The *ProPoints* values per serving will remain the same.

Butternut squash pâté

Butternut squash is very versatile and it's especially tasty in this fabulous pâté.

Ⓨ ❋ **Serves 6** ● **Takes 35** minutes + cooling
● **12 *ProPoints*** values per recipe

> 350 g (12 oz) butternut squash, *peeled, de-seeded and cut into chunks*
> 100 g (3½ oz) *dried* red lentils
> 600 ml (20 fl oz) *vegetable stock*
> 150 g (5½ oz) roasted red peppers in brine, *drained, patted dry and chopped*
> 100 g (3½ oz) *low fat soft cheese with garlic and herbs*
> *freshly ground black pepper*
> *raw vegetable crudités, such as* peppers, carrot *and* cucumber, *to serve*

Method

1 Put the squash and lentils in a lidded saucepan with the stock. Bring to the boil, then reduce the heat. Cover and simmer for 20–25 minutes or until the squash is tender and the lentils are soft.

2 Drain off any excess liquid thoroughly, using a colander or sieve. It's important that the ingredients are quite dry. Leave until completely cold.

3 Tip the squash and lentils into a bowl and add the red peppers and soft cheese. Use a hand held blender or food processor to blend the ingredients together until smooth. If you don't have a blender, use a potato masher instead.

4 Season the pâté with black pepper. Cover and chill until ready to eat. Serve 110 g (4 oz) per person with the vegetable crudités.

Ⓨ **Try this...** Serve 110 g (4 oz) pâté with four rye crispbreads per person for 6 ***ProPoints*** values per serving.

❋ **Tip...** You can keep the pâté in the refrigerator for up to 4 days in a covered container. If you like, freeze some of it and use within 2 months.

Jubilee chicken sandwich

A hint of curry gives this delicious sandwich a tasty kick.

Serves 2 ● Takes 10 minutes ● **16** *ProPoints* values per recipe

- 4 medium slices wholemeal bread
- 2 teaspoons low fat spread
- 2 tablespoons **low fat plain yogurt**
- ¼ teaspoon medium curry powder
- 2 teaspoons chopped **fresh coriander** (optional)
- 100 g (3½ oz) **skinless cooked chicken breast**, sliced
- 2 crisp **lettuce leaves**, shredded
- ¼ small red **onion** or 1 **spring onion**, sliced thinly
- 75 g (2¾ oz) **roasted red peppers in brine**, sliced
- salt and freshly ground black pepper

Method

1 Spread each slice of bread with the low fat spread.

2 Mix together the yogurt and curry powder, then stir in the coriander, if using. Add the chicken slices, tossing to coat in the mixture.

3 Share the lettuce between two slices of bread, then arrange the chicken on top. Sprinkle with the onion then share the red pepper between them.

4 Season, sandwich together with the remaining bread, then cut in half. Serve at once, or wrap in cling film and keep chilled to eat later.

Tip... Make sure you don't add too much curry powder. If you'd like it to be milder, simply add a generous pinch, or use a mild curry powder instead.

Curried chicken soup

❄ **Serves 4 ● Takes 25** minutes to prepare, **25** minutes to cook ● **21** *ProPoints* values per recipe

- low fat cooking spray
- 250 g (9 oz) **skinless boneless chicken breast**, cut into chunks
- 1 large **onion**, chopped
- 1 large **carrot**, peeled and chopped finely
- 1 eating **apple**, unpeeled, cored and chopped
- 1 **garlic clove**, crushed
- 2 tablespoons Tikka Masala curry paste
- 2 tablespoons tomato purée
- 75 g (2¾ oz) dried **yellow split peas**
- 850 ml (1½ pints) chicken or vegetable stock
- 50 g (1¾ oz) frozen **peas**
- 2 tablespoons chopped **fresh coriander**
- freshly ground black pepper

Method

1 Heat a large lidded saucepan until hot and spray with the cooking spray. Gently fry the chicken for 2–3 minutes until lightly browned, then add the onion, carrot, apple and garlic and cook for another 1–2 minutes. Add the curry paste and fry gently for a few seconds.

2 Stir in the tomato purée, split peas and stock, then bring up to the boil. Reduce the heat, then cover and simmer for about 25 minutes or until the split peas are tender and the soup has thickened.

3 Add the peas and coriander. Simmer gently for another 2–3 minutes. Season to taste and then ladle the soup into warmed bowls. Serve immediately.

Ⓥ **Try this...** For a vegetarian version of this recipe, use vegetable stock and substitute 200 g (7 oz) **Quorn Chicken Style Pieces** for the chicken, for the same *ProPoints* values per serving.

Deliciously warming and **aromatic**

5
ProPoints
value

Salmon and cucumber wrap

Soft flour tortillas make lovely wraps and a welcome change from sandwiches and rolls.

Serves 1 ● **Takes 10** minutes ● **9** *ProPoints* values per recipe

> 1 medium soft flour tortilla
> 1 tablespoon low fat soft cheese
> 105 g can **red salmon**, drained
> 2.5 cm (1 inch) **cucumber**, chopped finely
> a handful of **watercress** or shredded **lettuce**
> salt and freshly ground black pepper

Method

1 Put the tortilla on a clean worktop and spread the soft cheese over the top.

2 Remove the skin from the salmon but retain any softened bones as these are edible. Put in a bowl, mash with a fork and spread the salmon evenly over the cheese, then scatter the cucumber on top.

3 Add the watercress or lettuce, season to taste, then roll up the tortilla. Slice in half with a sharp knife, then serve.

● **Try this...** If you have some, sprinkle a little chopped **fresh dill**, **chives** or **parsley** over the **salmon** to add a little more flavour, for no additional *ProPoints* values. Also, try using low fat soft cheese with garlic and herbs instead of plain. The *ProPoints* values will remain the same.

Egg and cress bagel

Take a favourite combination, add a twist of imagination, and you have a very tasty lunch.

● **Serves 1** ● **Takes 15** minutes ● **8** *ProPoints* values per recipe

> 1 **egg**
> 1 sesame seed bagel, halved
> 1 tablespoon low fat soft cheese
> 1 **tomato**, sliced
> a handful of **cress**
> salt and freshly ground black pepper

Method

1 Bring a small saucepan of water to the boil, add the egg, reduce the heat and cook in simmering water for 12 minutes, then place it in cold water to cool quickly.

2 Meanwhile, toast the bagel halves lightly, then spread the cut surfaces with the soft cheese. Arrange the sliced tomatoes on top of the cheese on one bagel half.

3 Thinly slice the egg with a sharp knife, or use an egg slicer, then arrange on top of the tomatoes. Season to taste. Scatter the cress over the top, then sandwich the bagel top in place. Serve at once, or wrap in cling film and keep chilled until lunchtime.

● **Try this...** If you don't have a box of **cress**, finish off the bagels with chopped **fresh parsley**, **chives** or **spring onion** instead. The *ProPoints* values will remain the same.

Cheddar sandwich with beetroot slaw

Liven up a plain cheese sandwich with some carrot and beetroot coleslaw.

Ⓥ Serves 2 ● **Takes 10** minutes ● **16** *ProPoints* values per recipe

- 4 medium slices wholemeal bread
- 2 teaspoons low fat spread
- 50 g (1¾ oz) half fat Cheddar cheese, grated
- 1 small carrot, peeled and grated
- 1 small cooked beetroot, grated
- 25 g (1 oz) raisins or sultanas
- a few drops of cider or white wine vinegar
- a pinch of cumin seeds (optional)
- 2 tablespoons low fat plain yogurt
- salt and freshly ground black pepper

Method

1 Spread each slice of bread with the low fat spread. Share the cheese equally between them.

2 Put the carrot, beetroot and raisins or sultanas into a small bowl and add a few drops of cider or vinegar and the cumin seeds, if using. Season, then add the yogurt and stir to mix. Pile an equal amount on to the cheese.

3 Place the remaining bread slices on top and cut the sandwiches in half. Serve immediately or wrap and chill to serve later.

Ⓥ Try this... You could use grated celeriac instead of beetroot, for a change. You'll need 75 g (2¾ oz) for the recipe. The *ProPoints* values per serving will remain the same.

Creamy broccoli and spinach soup

2 ProPoints value

This easy soup tastes simply lovely.

Ⓥ ❄ **Serves 4** ● **Takes 20** minutes to prepare, **20** minutes to cook ● **8** *ProPoints* values per recipe

- 250 g (9 oz) **broccoli**, broken into florets
- 1 large **leek**, sliced
- 1 **onion**, chopped
- 250 g (9 oz) **potatoes**, peeled and chopped
- 1 litre (1¾ pints) vegetable stock
- 100 g (3½ oz) **spinach**, washed
- 75 g (2¾ oz) low fat soft cheese with garlic and herbs
- freshly ground black pepper

Method

1 Put the broccoli, leek, onion and potatoes in a large lidded saucepan and add the stock. Bring up to the boil, then cover and simmer for 20 minutes, until the vegetables are tender.

2 Add the spinach to the saucepan, stir it in and then remove from the heat. Adding the leaves at this stage gives the finished soup a beautiful, bright green colour.

3 Transfer the soup to a liquidiser or use a hand held blender. Add the soft cheese, then blend until smooth. Reheat, then season with black pepper, to taste. Serve in warmed bowls.

Ⓥ **Try this...** Instead of using low fat soft cheese with garlic and herbs, you could try plain low fat soft cheese and add a crushed **garlic clove** in step 1, with 1 tablespoon of chopped fresh herbs, such as **parsley**, **thyme** or **rosemary**, for the same *ProPoints* values.

New potato and tuna salad

7 ProPoints value

Serves 2 ● **Takes 25** minutes to prepare + cooling ● **14** *ProPoints* values per recipe

- 350 g (12 oz) Charlotte or new **potatoes**, scrubbed
- 125 g (4½ oz) fine **green beans**, trimmed and halved
- 2 teaspoons olive oil
- 1 tablespoon lemon juice
- 1 teaspoon finely chopped **fresh dill** or **parsley**
- 1 teaspoon wholegrain mustard
- ½ small red **onion**, sliced thinly
- 6 **cherry tomatoes**, halved
- ¼ **cucumber**, chopped
- 10 black or green olives in brine
- 185 g can **tuna in water or brine**, drained
- salt and freshly ground black pepper

Method

1 Put the potatoes in a saucepan, cover with cold water and bring the water to the boil. Cook for about 20 minutes or until tender. Drain.

2 Meanwhile, bring a separate pan of water to the boil. Add the green beans and cook for 4–5 minutes, or until just tender. Drain and rinse with cold water.

3 In a serving bowl, mix together the olive oil, lemon juice, dill or parsley and mustard. Season. Add the hot cooked potatoes to the dressing and then let them cool in the dressing so they absorb more of its flavour. Stir occasionally.

4 Add the green beans, onion, tomatoes, cucumber and olives to the cooled potatoes. Break the tuna into chunks and stir it through gently, so it doesn't break up too much. Serve immediately.

Ⓥ **Try this...** For a vegetarian alternative, omit the **tuna** and add 50 g (1¾ oz) half fat Cheddar cheese, cut into small cubes. The *ProPoints* values will remain the same.

Pack up a tasty and **filling lunch** to enjoy at work

Cullen skink

This British version of American fish chowder makes a marvellous meal in a bowl.

❄ **Serves 4** ● **Takes 15** minutes to prepare, **25** minutes to cook ● **19** *ProPoints* values per recipe

> 1 large **onion**, chopped finely
> 1 large **leek**, sliced thinly
> 250 g (9 oz) floury **potatoes**, peeled and
>   cut into small chunks
> 600 ml (20 fl oz) chicken or vegetable stock
> 250 g (9 oz) skinless **smoked haddock**,
>   cut into chunks
> 2 tablespoons cornflour
> 300 ml (10 fl oz) **skimmed milk**
> 2 tablespoons chopped **fresh parsley**
> freshly ground black pepper

Method

1 Put the onion, leek, potatoes and stock in a lidded saucepan. Bring up to the boil, then cover and simmer for about 25 minutes or until the potatoes are very tender and starting to break up.
2 Add the haddock and cook for a further 2–3 minutes.
3 Meanwhile, blend the cornflour with 3 tablespoons of the milk. Pour the remaining milk into the saucepan and heat gently.
4 Add the blended cornflour to the soup and heat, stirring constantly, until thickened. Add the parsley, season with black pepper, then serve.

Carrot and red lentil soup

A hint of ginger and chilli gives this a fiery kick.

Ⓥ ❄ **Serves 6** ● **Takes 10** minutes to prepare, **30** minutes to cook ● **17** *ProPoints* values per recipe

> 1 large **onion**, chopped
> 700 g (1 lb 9 oz) **carrots**, peeled and chopped
> 150 g (5½ oz) dried **red lentils**
> 2 teaspoons chopped fresh red **chilli** or
>   1 teaspoon medium chilli powder
> ½ teaspoon ground ginger
> 1.5 litres (2¾ pints) vegetable stock
> 6 tablespoons **low fat plain yogurt**
> salt and freshly ground black pepper

Method

1 Put the onion, carrots, lentils, chilli, ginger and stock in a large lidded saucepan. Bring up to the boil, then reduce the heat. Cover and simmer for 25–30 minutes until the lentils and vegetables are tender.
2 Transfer the soup to a liquidiser, or use a hand held blender, and blend until smooth, then return it to the saucepan. Reheat then season to taste.
3 Ladle the soup into warmed bowls and top each serving with 1 tablespoon of yogurt and some extra black pepper.

❄ **Tips...** The soup can be frozen for up to 3 months or chilled for up to 3 days.

... If you prefer a chunky soup, there's no need to blend it.

Cook's ideas...
Get into the habit of soup all year round. Try to keep some in the freezer. If you like, create a smooth texture with a hand held blender.

Fruity chicken and rice salad

8 ProPoints value

This makes a great buffet salad too. For eight people, it will be 4 *ProPoints* values per serving.

Serves 4 ● **Takes 15** minutes to prepare, **20** minutes to cook ● **32** *ProPoints* values per recipe

- 200 g (7 oz) dried long grain rice
- 1 vegetable stock cube, crumbled
- 225 g (8 oz) **skinless cooked chicken breast**, chopped
- 227 g can **pineapple pieces in natural juice**, drained
- 150 g (5½ oz) red and green seedless **grapes**, halved
- 25 g (1 oz) sultanas or raisins
- 50 g (1¾ oz) ready to eat, semi-dried apricots, chopped
- a squeeze of lemon juice
- a few **mint leaves**, torn into pieces (optional)
- freshly ground black pepper

Method

1 Bring a pan of water to the boil, add the rice with the crumbled stock cube and cook according to the packet instructions until tender. Drain, rinse with cold water to cool quickly, then drain thoroughly.

2 Tip the rice into a large serving bowl and add the chicken, all the fruit and then squeeze in the lemon juice. Add the mint leaves, if using, then stir gently to mix all the ingredients together. Season with black pepper.

3 Share between four plates or bowls and then serve at once.

Tip... Keep any leftovers in a covered container in the fridge and use within two days.

Bubble and squeak |6| ProPoints value

This favourite works a treat with a poached egg, served on top of each portion, for an additional 2 *ProPoints* values per serving.

Ⓥ ❋ **Serves 2** ● **Takes 30** minutes ● **12** *ProPoints* values per recipe

> 300 g (10½ oz) **potatoes**, peeled and chopped
> 75 g (2¾ oz) **cabbage**, chopped
> a pinch of caraway seeds (optional)
> 2 smoked lean back bacon rashers, chopped
> 3 **spring onions**, chopped finely
> 1 small **garlic clove**, crushed
> 1 **egg**, beaten
> low fat cooking spray
> salt and freshly ground black pepper

Method

1 Put the potatoes in a lidded saucepan, cover with cold water and bring to the boil. Cover and cook until tender. Drain thoroughly. At the same time, put the cabbage in a separate saucepan, cover with cold water and cook until tender. Mash the potatoes and then mix them together with the cooked cabbage, adding the caraway seeds, if using.
2 Dry fry the bacon in a non stick frying pan for about 3 minutes, stirring often. Add the spring onions and garlic and cook for another 2 minutes, until softened. Add to the potatoes and cabbage, mix well and then add half the beaten egg and a little seasoning, mixing thoroughly with your hands.
3 Form the mixture into four triangles or rounds, then dip them into (or brush them with) the remaining beaten egg.
4 Heat a non stick frying pan until hot and spray with the cooking spray. Add the potato cakes, cooking them over a medium heat until browned on both sides. Serve immediately.

Ⓥ **Try this...** For a vegetarian option, leave out the bacon. The *ProPoints* values per serving will be 4.

Leek and ham gratins |5| ProPoints value

Serves 2 ● **Takes 20** minutes ● **9** *ProPoints* values per recipe

> 1 teaspoon half fat butter
> 1 teaspoon Dijon mustard
> 1 large **leek**, sliced
> 125 g (4½ oz) young **spinach**, washed
> 75 g (2¾ oz) sliced **roast ham**
> 125 g (4½ oz) low fat soft cheese with garlic and herbs
> 40 g (1½ oz) half fat mature Cheddar cheese, grated
> freshly ground black pepper

Method

1 Mix together the butter and the mustard. Smear the mixture around the base and sides of two 20 cm (8 inch) x 12 cm (4½ inch) shallow ovenproof serving dishes.
2 Bring a pan of water to the boil, add the leeks and cook for about 5 minutes until soft. Meanwhile, in another saucepan, bring a small amount of water to the boil and cook the spinach for 2–3 minutes, until the leaves wilt. Drain the spinach and press out the excess liquid in it with the back of a spoon.
3 Reserve 4 tablespoons of the cooking liquid from the leeks, then drain them thoroughly. Divide the leeks and spinach between the two dishes. Tear up the ham and add it to the dishes, mixing it with the vegetables. Preheat the grill to medium high.
4 Tip the soft cheese into a bowl and use a wooden spoon to beat until smooth. Gradually add the reserved cooking liquid to make a smooth sauce. Pour an equal amount over each dish. Season with black pepper then sprinkle the grated cheese evenly over the top of each.
5 Grill for 6–8 minutes until browned and bubbling.

Ⓥ **Try this...** For a vegetarian version, omit the ham and add an extra 40 g (1½ oz) half fat mature Cheddar cheese for the same *ProPoints* values per serving.

Ready in **just 20 minutes**

traditional suppers

Enjoy an exciting selection of tasty traditional meals.

When nothing but real comfort food will do, turn to these **wonderfully warming, tried and tested suppers.** Fancy a delicious plate of Baked Fish and Chips or Good Shepherd's Pie? Go ahead – tuck in and enjoy.

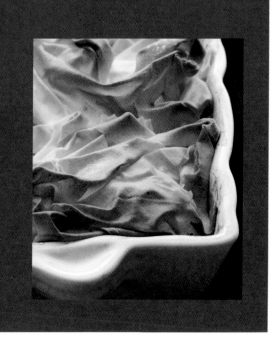

Filo turkey pie

Serves 4 ● **Takes 35** minutes to prepare,
25 minutes to cook ● **34** *ProPoints* values per recipe

150 g (5½ oz) broccoli, broken into small florets
100 g (3½ oz) fine green beans, trimmed
    and sliced
low fat cooking spray
400 g (14 oz) skinless boneless turkey breast,
    cut into chunks
4 spring onions, trimmed and chopped
1 red pepper, de-seeded and chopped
150 ml (5 fl oz) dry white wine
1 tablespoon chopped fresh parsley or thyme
1 tablespoon chicken gravy granules
6 x 45 g (1½ oz) filo pastry sheets,
    thawed if frozen
salt and freshly ground black pepper

Method

1 Preheat the oven to Gas Mark 6/200°C/fan oven 180°C.

2 Bring a pan of water to the boil, add the broccoli and beans and cook for 4–5 minutes. Drain well, then tip them into a 1.5 litre (2¾ pint) baking dish.

3 Heat a wok or large non stick frying pan until hot. Spray with the cooking spray. Add the turkey and stir fry over a high heat for 4–5 minutes until browned then add to the baking dish.

4 Spray the wok or frying pan again with the cooking spray and stir fry the spring onions and pepper for 3–4 minutes, until softened. Add them to the baking dish. Pour the wine into the wok or frying pan and heat until bubbling. Add 225 ml (8 fl oz) water and the parsley or thyme. Heat until boiling, then add the gravy granules, stirring until thickened. Pour over the turkey and vegetables in the baking dish, stirring gently to mix. Season.

5 Spray each sheet of filo pastry with the cooking spray and arrange on top of the turkey mixture, scrunching them up to fit. Bake for 20–25 minutes, until golden brown. Serve immediately.

Lancashire lobscouse [8 ProPoints value]

Chicken in red wine [5 ProPoints value]

With just three ingredients and a little seasoning, it's hard to believe this dish tastes so incredibly good – yet it does.

Serves 4 ● **Takes 20** minutes to prepare,
2 hours to cook ● **33 ProPoints** values per recipe

> 400 g (14 oz) **lean braising steak** or **stewing steak**, visible fat removed, cut into chunks
> 1 large **onion**, chopped
> 1 kg (2 lb 4 oz) **potatoes**, peeled and chopped into small pieces
> freshly ground black pepper

Method

1 Heat a large, lidded, flameproof casserole dish or a large lidded saucepan until hot. Add the steak, cooking it over a high heat for about 2 minutes until seared (there is no need for cooking spray). Add 1 litre (1¾ pints) of water. Bring up to the boil, then cover tightly and reduce the heat to very low. Cook for about 1½ hours or until the meat is very tender.
2 Add the onion, cover and cook for a further 15 minutes.
3 Add the potatoes, cover and cook for a further 15–20 minutes, until tender. Season with black pepper then serve in warmed bowls.

Serving suggestions... The lobscouse tastes great topped with **pickled red cabbage** or **pickled silverskin onions** for no extra **ProPoints** values. Tomato ketchup or brown sauce goes with it too, but remember to add 1 **ProPoints** value for every 2 tablespoons used.

Serve with six 225 g (8 oz) potatoes, baked in their skins at the same time on the shelf above, for an additional 5 **ProPoints** values per serving.

❋ **Serves 6** ● **Takes 20** minutes to prepare,
1¼ hours to cook ● **30 ProPoints** values per recipe

> low fat cooking spray
> 6 **skinless boneless chicken breasts** (750 g/1 lb 10 oz in total)
> 1 smoked lean back bacon rasher, chopped
> 12 **shallots**, left whole, or 1 large **onion**, chopped
> 1 **garlic clove**, crushed
> 1 **leek**, sliced
> 250 g (9 oz) **mushrooms**, halved
> 450 g (1 lb) small **carrots**, peeled, trimmed and halved
> 350 ml (12 fl oz) red wine
> 700 ml (1¼ pints) chicken stock
> 1 teaspoon dried tarragon or thyme
> 2 bay leaves
> 2 tablespoons chopped **fresh parsley**
> salt and freshly ground black pepper

Method

1 Preheat the oven to Gas Mark 4/180°C/fan oven 160°C. Heat a large, lidded, flameproof casserole dish until hot. Spray with the cooking spray.
2 Add the chicken breasts, letting them sear and brown before turning them over. Cook for 3–4 minutes until browned on both sides. (Alternatively, brown the chicken in a non stick frying pan first, then transfer to a regular casserole dish).
3 Add the bacon, shallots or onion, garlic, leek, mushrooms and carrots. Pour in the wine and stock, then add all the herbs. Season and cover.
4 Transfer to the oven and bake for 1–1¼ hours. Remove the bay leaves, then serve.

Cook's ideas...
Invest in the right cookware. Good quality non stick pans, flameproof casseroles and microwave safe dishes make cooking easier.

Toad in the hole

These individual servings are delicious with plenty of lightly cooked vegetables, such as carrots, cabbage, green beans or broccoli, for no additional *ProPoints* values per serving.

Serves 4 ● **Takes 15** minutes to prepare, **20** minutes to cook ● **24** *ProPoints* values per recipe

    2 teaspoons vegetable oil
    4 low fat sausages (such as Weight Watchers
        Premium Pork Sausages)

For the batter
75 g (2¾ oz) plain flour
a pinch of salt
1 egg
200 ml (7 fl oz) skimmed milk

For the gravy
1 small onion, chopped finely
100 g (3½ oz) mushrooms, sliced thinly
425 ml (15 fl oz) boiling water
2 tablespoons beef or chicken gravy granules
freshly ground black pepper

Method

1 Preheat the oven to Gas Mark 6/200°C/fan oven 180°C.

2 Put ½ a teaspoon of oil into each hole of a four hole Yorkshire pudding tin and then add a sausage to each. Heat in the oven for 10 minutes.

3 Meanwhile, make the batter. Sift the flour and salt into a large jug or mixing bowl. Add the egg and milk and beat with a wire whisk until smooth. Pour carefully around the sausages and return to the oven as quickly as possible. Bake for 20 minutes until puffed up and golden brown.

4 While they are cooking, make the gravy. Put the onion and mushrooms into a saucepan with the boiling water. Simmer for 15 minutes then add the gravy granules, stirring until thickened. Season with some black pepper.

5 Remove from the tin and serve each toad on a warmed plate with the gravy spooned over.

Ⓥ Try this... Use four vegetarian sausages instead of pork and make the gravy with vegetarian gravy granules, for the same *ProPoints* values per serving.

Rosti fish pie

Serves 4 ● Takes 20 minutes to prepare,
25 minutes to cook ● **43** *ProPoints* values per recipe

    1 kg (2 lb 4 oz) **potatoes**, peeled and cut
        into large chunks
    350 g (12 oz) frozen mixed **vegetables**
    1 tablespoon plain flour
    2 tablespoons chopped **fresh parsley** or
        chives
    320 g pack mixed **fish chunks** (or fresh
        from the fish counter)
    300 g (10½ oz) half fat crème fraîche
    salt and freshly ground black pepper

Method

1 Bring a pan of water to the boil, add the potatoes
and cook for 15 minutes or until just tender. Drain
well and leave to cool.

2 Meanwhile, bring another pan of water to the
boil, add the vegetables and cook for 2–3 minutes,
until they are no longer frozen. Drain really well,
then tip into a 1.2 litre (2 pint) shallow baking dish.
Preheat the oven to Gas Mark 5/190°C/fan oven
170°C.

3 Sprinkle the flour on to a plate and season. Add
the parsley or chives, then mix in the fish chunks,
tossing to coat. Transfer them to the baking dish
and mix with the vegetables. Add the crème fraîche,
mixing it in gently.

4 Coarsely grate the potatoes and season with
some black pepper. Arrange evenly over the fish
mixture. Bake for 20–25 minutes, until browned and
piping hot. Serve immediately.

Try this... If you're in a hurry, you can mash the
potatoes and spoon them on top of the fish.

Tip... To brown the top of the fish pie a bit more,
place it under a hot grill for a few minutes.

Baked fish and spicy chips

Why not stick with tradition and serve with a
50 g (1¾ oz) portion of mushy peas for a further
1 *ProPoints* value?

❋ **Serves 1 ● Takes 10** minutes to prepare,
40 minutes to cook ● **14** *ProPoints* values per recipe

    250 g (9 oz) **potato**, cut into 8 wedges
    low fat cooking spray
    ½ teaspoon Cajun seasoning or paprika
    25 g (1 oz) couscous
    ½ a kettleful of boiling water
    200 g (7 oz) **skinless haddock**
    1 **egg**, beaten
    salt and freshly ground black pepper

Method

1 Preheat the oven to Gas Mark 6/200°C/fan oven
180°C.

2 Put the potato wedges on a baking tray and
spray them with the cooking spray. Sprinkle with the
Cajun seasoning or paprika and season. Transfer
to the middle shelf of the oven to bake for 35–40
minutes, turning them over after 20 minutes.

3 Meanwhile, put the couscous into a heatproof
bowl and add just enough boiling water to cover it.
Leave to soak for about 5 minutes until swollen. Fluff
up the grains with a fork, then sprinkle them on to a
plate. Season.

4 Dip the haddock into the beaten egg, then coat it
in the couscous. Put it on a baking tray then transfer
it to the oven when you turn the potatoes, placing
it on the shelf above, and cook for 15–20 minutes.
Serve with the spicy chips.

Try this... If you're on a budget, try **pollock** instead
for 13 *ProPoints* values per serving.

Or this... Use 25 g (1 oz) dried breadcrumbs
instead of couscous. The *ProPoints* values per
serving will remain the same.

Fabulous **fish and chips**

Lamb and barley stew

Cabbage, green beans or broccoli are ideal on the side for no additional *ProPoints* values.

❋ **Serves 4** ● **Takes 20** minutes to prepare, **1** hour to cook ● **28** *ProPoints* values per recipe

low fat cooking spray
350 g (12 oz) lean lamb (such as leg
    or rump), visible fat removed, cut
    into chunks
1 **onion**, chopped
2 **carrots**, peeled and sliced
2 **celery sticks**, sliced
200 g (7 oz) **swede**, peeled and chopped
1 **parsnip**, peeled and chopped
1 **leek**, sliced
850 ml (1½ pints) lamb or chicken stock
75 g (2¾ oz) dried pearl barley, rinsed
    with boiling water
1 **fresh rosemary sprig**
3 tablespoons chopped **fresh parsley**
salt and freshly ground black pepper

Method

1 Heat a large, lidded, heavy based saucepan until hot and spray with cooking spray. Add the lamb, searing it over a high heat for a few moments before turning it over. Stir and then allow another 2 minutes or so for them to brown (this adds a lot of flavour to the stew). You may need to do this in batches.

2 Add the onion, carrots, celery, swede, parsnip and leek to the saucepan. Pour in the stock and add the pearl barley, rosemary and 2 tablespoons of parsley. Season. Bring up to the boil, cover and reduce the heat.

3 Simmer the stew for 1 hour, stirring from time to time, until the vegetables are tender and the pearl barley is plump and soft. Add a little extra stock or water if necessary.

4 Remove the rosemary sprig, check the seasoning and then serve in warmed bowls, sprinkled with the remaining parsley.

Good shepherd's pie

Try this veggie version of a family favourite.

Ⓨ ❄ **Serves 4 ● Takes 20** minutes to prepare,
25 minutes to cook ● **24** *ProPoints* values per recipe

- *500 g (1 lb 2 oz)* **potatoes**, *peeled and cut into large chunks*
- *500 g (1 lb 2 oz)* **celeriac**, *peeled and cut into large chunks*
- *low fat cooking spray*
- *1* **onion**, *chopped finely*
- *1* **carrot**, *peeled and diced*
- *1* **parsnip**, *peeled and diced*
- *150 g (5½ oz)* **swede** *or* **turnip**, *peeled and diced*
- *300 g pack frozen* **Quorn mince**
- *425 ml (15 fl oz) vegetable stock*
- *50 g (1¾ oz) frozen* **peas**
- *1 tablespoon cornflour*
- *salt and freshly ground black pepper*

Method

1 Bring a large pan of water to the boil. Add the potatoes and celeriac and cook for 20 minutes until tender.

2 Meanwhile, heat a large, lidded, non stick saucepan until hot and spray with the cooking spray. Add the onion, carrot, parsnip and swede or turnip and stir fry for 4–5 minutes. Add the Quorn mince and stock. Cover and cook over a low heat for 25 minutes, adding the peas for the final 5 minutes.

3 Preheat the grill to medium high. Warm a 1.5 litre (2¾ pint) baking dish under the grill.

4 Drain the potatoes and celeriac, then return to the pan and mash. Season to taste. Blend the cornflour with 2 tablespoons of cold water and add to the Quorn mixture, stirring until thickened.

5 Tip the mixture into the baking dish and spoon the potato mixture on top to cover the surface. Grill for about 5–6 minutes until browned. Serve at once.

6 ProPoints value

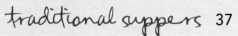

Bacon and onion hotpot

This easy savoury bake has just four main ingredients so it's very economical. Serve with carrots, broccoli, lightly cooked cabbage or kale for no additional *ProPoints* values.

Serves 2 ● Takes 15 minutes to prepare, **1¼** hours to cook ● **18 *ProPoints*** values per recipe

> 500 g (1 lb 2 oz) potatoes, peeled and
>   sliced thinly
> 1 large onion, sliced thinly
> 500 ml (18 fl oz) chicken or vegetable stock
> 4 lean back bacon rashers
> salt and freshly ground black pepper
> 2 tablespoons tomato ketchup, to serve

Method

1 Preheat the oven to Gas Mark 5/190°C/fan oven 170°C.

2 Arrange the potato and onion slices in alternating layers in a 1.5 litre (2¾ pint) baking or casserole dish, seasoning each layer and finishing with a layer of potatoes. Pour in the stock.

3 Transfer to the oven and bake, uncovered, for 1 hour. Arrange the bacon rashers on top and bake for another 15 minutes. The potatoes should be tender, and the top layer of potatoes and the bacon should be crisp.

4 Serve on warmed plates with 1 tablespoon of tomato ketchup for each portion.

Tip... If you have one, a shallow baking dish works better than a deep one.

Steak and mushroom pies

❄ Before baking **Serves 4 ● Takes 25** minutes to prepare, **2** hours to cook ● **33 *ProPoints*** values per recipe

> low fat cooking spray
> 400 g (14 oz) lean braising or stewing steak,
>   visible fat removed, cut into chunks
> 1 onion, chopped
> 200 g (7 oz) mushrooms, sliced
> 3 tablespoons Worcestershire sauce
> 425 ml (15 fl oz) beef stock
> 3 tablespoons cornflour
> 2 tablespoons chopped fresh parsley
> 4 x 8 cm (3¼ inch) squares of ready rolled
>   puff pastry (100 g/3½ oz in total)
> 2 teaspoons skimmed milk
> salt and freshly ground black pepper

Method

1 Heat a heavy based, lidded, non stick saucepan until hot and spray with cooking spray. Add the beef in batches, searing it over a high heat until browned on all sides.

2 Add the onion, mushrooms, Worcestershire sauce and stock. Bring to the boil, cover with a tight fitting lid and reduce the heat to very low. Simmer for about 1½ hours until the meat is tender. Check regularly and add water, if needed. Preheat the oven to Gas Mark 7/220°C/fan oven 200°C.

3 Blend the cornflour with 3 tablespoons of cold water. Add to the saucepan and stir until thickened. Add the parsley and check the seasoning. Spoon the mixture into four individual baking dishes and reserve the excess gravy in the pan. Cool the mixture for 10 minutes.

4 Place the pastry squares on top of each dish and brush over a little milk. Cut a slit in the top of each with a sharp knife. Stand the dishes on a baking tray.

5 Bake for 20–25 minutes until golden brown. Serve immediately with the reheated gravy.

Smoked pollock kedgeree

This inexpensive and easy recipe is ideal for a weeknight supper.

Serves 4 ● **Takes 45** minutes ● **43** *ProPoints* values per recipe

   250 g (9 oz) dried long grain brown rice
   1.2 litres (2 pints) vegetable stock
   4 eggs
   200 g (7 oz) skinless smoked pollock fillet
   100 g (3½ oz) skinless salmon fillet
   low fat cooking spray
   a bunch of spring onions, trimmed
      and chopped
   1 teaspoon cumin seeds
   75 g (2¾ oz) frozen petit pois, thawed
   salt and freshly ground black pepper
   2 tablespoons chopped fresh coriander,
      plus sprigs, to garnish

Method

1 Put the rice and stock into a large lidded saucepan and bring to the boil. Cover, reduce the heat and cook according to the packet instructions until tender, adding extra water if needed.

Meanwhile, bring another pan of water to the boil, add the eggs and cook for 12 minutes to hard boil.
2 Put the pollock and salmon in a large frying pan or wok. Add enough water to just cover the fish. Heat and simmer for 5–6 minutes until the fish is cooked. The flesh should be opaque and flake easily. Drain and cool, then flake into large chunks. Set aside.
3 Spray a non stick frying pan or wok with the cooking spray and add the spring onions. Cook gently for 4–5 minutes, without browning, then add the cumin seeds and peas. Cook for a few moments. Drain the rice thoroughly and add it to the pan, then gently stir in the fish and coriander. Season.
4 Share the mixture between four warmed plates. Shell and quarter the eggs and arrange them on top of the kedgeree. Serve sprinkled with a little more black pepper and garnished with coriander sprigs.

Try this... You can use smoked haddock instead of pollock for the same *ProPoints* values per serving.

modern suppers

Serve up some tasty supper dishes, with a modern slant.

These meals **celebrate our contemporary tastes** – the love of spice and a desire to enjoy new ingredients and combinations. So why not try recipes such as Chorizo Lasagne or Turkey Stir Fry and liven up suppertime tonight?

Seared salmon and horseradish mash

13 ProPoints value

Simple salmon with a tasty mash is just the thing for a weekday supper.

Serves 2 ● Takes 25 minutes ● **25** *ProPoints* values per recipe

> 450 g (1 lb) potatoes, peeled and cut into chunks
> 4 spring onions, sliced finely
> low fat cooking spray
> 2 x 150 g (5½ oz) salmon fillets
> 2 tablespoons skimmed milk
> 1 tablespoon horseradish sauce
> 2 tablespoons chopped fresh parsley
> salt and freshly ground black pepper

> To garnish
> 2 lemon wedges
> a handful of fresh parsley sprigs

Method

1 Bring a saucepan of water to the boil. Add the potatoes and cook for 20 minutes or until tender, adding the spring onions to the saucepan 5 minutes before the end of cooking time.

2 Once the potatoes have been cooking for 10 minutes, start to prepare the salmon. Spray a non stick frying pan with the cooking spray and heat. When hot, add the salmon, skin side down. Cook over a high heat for 3 minutes, without moving the fillets. This will sear the skin and make it nice and crisp. Turn the salmon over, reduce the heat and cook for a further 3–4 minutes. Turn off the heat and let the salmon rest while you make the mash.

3 Drain the potatoes and spring onions, then mash thoroughly. Beat in the milk, add the horseradish sauce and parsley and season. Beat until fluffy.

4 Share the mash between two warmed plates and sit the salmon fillets on top. Serve each dish garnished with a lemon wedge and parsley.

Chilli con carne

※ Chilli only **Serves 2 ● Takes 45** minutes
● **19 ProPoints** values per recipe

> 225 g (8 oz) extra lean beef mince
> 1 small **onion**, chopped
> 1 **garlic clove**, crushed
> 1 small fresh red **chilli**, de-seeded and
>   chopped finely
> 1 small **carrot**, peeled and chopped
> 1 red **pepper**, de-seeded and chopped
> 150 ml (5 fl oz) beef or vegetable stock
> 200 g (7 oz) canned chopped **tomatoes**
> 125 g (4½ oz) canned **mixed pulses**,
>   rinsed and drained
> 2 tablespoons tomato purée
> 100 g (3½ oz) **mushrooms**, sliced
> 1 **tomato**, chopped finely
> 5 cm (2 inch) **cucumber**, chopped finely
> ½ small red **onion**, chopped finely
> 1 tablespoon chopped **fresh parsley**
> a squeeze of lemon juice
> 1 medium size soft flour tortilla

Method

1 Heat a large, lidded, heavy based saucepan until hot. Add the mince, a little at a time. Let it sear over a high heat, then stir after 30–40 seconds and cook for another 1–2 minutes until browned.

2 Add the onion, garlic, chilli, carrot and pepper. Cook, stirring, for a further 2–3 minutes.

3 Pour in the stock, tip in the tomatoes and pulses, then add the tomato purée and mushrooms. Stir well. Cover and simmer for 25–30 minutes.

4 Meanwhile, make the salsa. Mix together the tomato, cucumber, red onion and parsley in a small serving bowl. Squeeze in some lemon juice.

5 Ten minutes before serving, preheat the grill to medium high. Cut the tortilla into eight triangles and arrange them on a baking tray. Grill lightly until crisp and golden, turning once. Allow to cool.

6 Serve the chilli with the salsa and four tortilla chips each.

Chicken korma

※ Without banana **Serves 4 ● Takes 20** minutes to prepare, **35** minutes to cook ● **51 ProPoints** values per recipe

> low fat cooking spray
> 500 g (1 lb 2 oz) **skinless boneless chicken**
>   **breasts**, chopped into chunks
> 1 large **onion**, chopped
> 1 eating **apple**, peeled, cored and chopped
> 1 **garlic clove**, crushed
> 2 tablespoons korma curry paste
> 400 ml (14 fl oz) chicken or vegetable stock
> 25 g (1 oz) sultanas
> 250 g (9 oz) dried long grain **brown rice**
> 1 tablespoon cornflour
> 4 tablespoons **low fat plain yogurt**
> 1 **banana**
> salt and freshly ground black pepper
> a handful of chopped **fresh coriander**,
>   to garnish (optional)

Method

1 Spray a large lidded saucepan with the cooking spray. Add the chicken, onion, apple and garlic and stir fry for 2–3 minutes. Stir in the curry paste and cook for a few seconds.

2 Add the stock and sultanas. Bring up to the boil then reduce the heat and simmer, partially covered, for 35 minutes. Stir occasionally, adding a little more stock or water, if necessary.

3 Meanwhile, bring a pan of water to the boil. Add the rice and cook according to the packet instructions until tender. Drain.

4 Just before serving, add 2 tablespoons of cold water to the cornflour and blend. Add the blended cornflour to the curry, stirring until thickened. Add the yogurt and slice in the banana, cooking gently for a few moments. Check the seasoning and serve with the rice, garnished with coriander, if using.

Tuna and sweetcorn fish cakes

⊞ 10 ProPoints value

❄ Before baking **Serves 4 ● Takes 25** minutes to prepare + chilling, **25** minutes to bake
● **39 *ProPoints*** values per recipe

600 g (1 lb 5 oz) **potatoes**, peeled and
  cut into chunks
2 **eggs**
150 g (5½ oz) **sweetcorn**, thawed if frozen
2 tablespoons chopped **fresh parsley**
2 x 185 g cans **tuna in brine or water**, drained
low fat cooking spray
4 **spring onions**, chopped finely
2 tablespoons **skimmed milk**
1 tablespoon plain flour
75 g (2¾ oz) dried breadcrumbs
salt and freshly ground black pepper

Method

1 Bring a pan of water to the boil, add the potatoes and cook for 20 minutes or until tender. Drain and mash, then leave until cold.

2 Meanwhile, bring another pan of water to the boil, and cook one egg for 12 minutes. Cool in cold water, then shell and chop it. Mix it with the potatoes, sweetcorn and parsley. Break the tuna into chunks and add it to the mixture.

3 Preheat the oven to Gas Mark 5/190°C/fan oven 170°C. Spray a non stick frying pan with the cooking spray. Add the spring onions. Stir fry for 3 minutes, until softened. Add to the potato mixture with the milk and seasoning, mixing well with your hands. Form into eight fish cakes.

4 Beat the remaining egg in a shallow bowl. Sprinkle the flour and breadcrumbs on to separate plates. Dust the fish cakes lightly with flour, dip them into the egg, then coat in the breadcrumbs. Chill for 10 minutes.

5 Spray a non stick baking tray with the cooking spray and arrange the fish cakes on it. Bake for 20–25 minutes until golden brown.

Sausages with peppers and lentils

⊞ 6 ProPoints value

Ⓥ ❄ **Serves 4 ● Takes 20** minutes to prepare, **20** minutes to cook ● **25 *ProPoints*** values per recipe

8 vegetarian sausages
low fat cooking spray
1 **onion**, sliced thinly
1 large **leek**, sliced
1 large red **pepper**, de-seeded and chopped
1 large yellow or orange **pepper**, de-seeded
  and chopped
1 **carrot**, peeled and sliced thinly
100 g (3½ oz) **mushrooms**, halved
300 ml (10 fl oz) vegetable stock
2 tablespoons sun-dried tomato purée
1 tablespoon chopped **fresh rosemary**
  or 2 teaspoons dried rosemary
410 g can green **lentils**, rinsed and drained
freshly ground black pepper

Method

1 Preheat the oven to Gas Mark 5/190°C/fan oven 170°C

2 Put the sausages in a large baking or casserole dish and set to one side.

3 Heat a large non stick frying pan or wok and spray with the cooking spray. Add the onion, leek, peppers, carrot and mushrooms. Stir fry them for 5–6 minutes, until softened. Tip them into the baking dish.

4 Pour in the stock and add the tomato purée, rosemary and lentils. Mix well and season with black pepper.

5 Transfer the baking dish to the oven and bake for 20 minutes, uncovered, and serve.

Try this... You can use the same number of Weight Watchers Premium Pork sausages instead of the vegetarian ones. You'll need to brown them under the grill before adding the remaining ingredients. The ***ProPoints*** values per serving will be 7.

Comfort food at its **best**

Macaroni cheese with leeks

13 ProPoints value

The extra vegetables add lots of flavour.

Ⓥ ❄ Without the cherry tomatoes **Serves 2**
● **Takes 20** minutes ● **25** *ProPoints* values per recipe

> 150 g (5½ oz) dried macaroni
> 1 small **onion**, chopped finely
> 1 **leek**, sliced thinly
> 20 g (¾ oz) low fat spread
> 25 g (1 oz) plain flour
> 300 ml (10 fl oz) **skimmed milk**
> ½ teaspoon English mustard
> 50 g (1¾ oz) half fat Cheddar cheese, grated
> 12 **cherry tomatoes**, halved
> salt and freshly ground black pepper

Method

1 Bring a large lidded saucepan of water to the boil. Add the pasta and cook for 5 minutes then add the onion and leek. Cook for a further 4–5 minutes, or according to the packet instructions, until the pasta is tender.

2 Meanwhile, put the low fat spread, flour and milk in a non stick saucepan. Heat, stirring constantly with a small whisk, until thickened and smooth. This all-in-one method is the best way to make a smooth, lump free sauce. Remove from the heat and add the mustard and 25 g (1 oz) of the cheese. Season.

3 Preheat the grill to medium high. Warm two individual baking dishes or one larger dish underneath.

4 Drain the pasta and vegetables thoroughly (if too wet, they will make the sauce runny). Add to the hot cheese sauce and stir gently. Tip the mixture into the warmed baking dish and top with the cherry tomatoes. Sprinkle the reserved cheese over the top. Grill for 5–6 minutes until browned and piping hot, then serve immediately.

Cottage pie with potato thatch

8 ProPoints value

❄ **Serves 4** ● **Takes 30** minutes to prepare,
20 minutes to cook ● **30** *ProPoints* values per recipe

> 500 g (1 lb 2 oz) **potatoes**, peeled and cut into chunks
> 500 g (1 lb 2 oz) **butternut squash**, peeled, de-seeded and cut into chunks
> 400 g (14 oz) extra lean beef mince
> 1 **onion**, chopped finely
> 1 **carrot**, peeled and chopped finely
> 1 **courgette**, chopped finely
> 100 g (3½ oz) **mushrooms**, sliced
> 1 teaspoon dried mixed herbs
> 4 teaspoons beef gravy granules
> salt and freshly ground black pepper

Method

1 Bring a large saucepan of water to the boil. Add the potatoes and squash and cook for about 20 minutes or until tender.

2 Meanwhile, heat a large lidded saucepan and add the beef mince, a handful at a time. Cook it over a high heat until seared and browned.

3 Stir in the onion, carrot, courgette, mushrooms and mixed herbs. Add 400 ml (14 fl oz) water and bring up to the boil. Simmer, partially covered, for 20 minutes. Preheat the grill to medium high.

4 Warm a large baking dish under the grill for 1–2 minutes. Meanwhile, drain and mash the potatoes and squash then season.

5 Sprinkle the gravy granules into the beef mince mixture, stirring until thickened. Season, then tip into the baking dish. Spoon the mash on top, spreading it out to cover the mince. Grill until browned, then serve.

Ⓥ **Try this...** For a vegetarian version, use 400 g (14 oz) **Quorn mince** and vegetable gravy granules for 6 *ProPoints* values per serving.

Turkey stir fry

Ideal for a quiet night in.

Serves 1 ● Takes 25 minutes ● **12** *ProPoints* values
per recipe

> 3 tablespoons orange juice
> 1 tablespoon soy sauce
> 1 tablespoon sweet chilli sauce
> 1 teaspoon cornflour
> low fat cooking spray
> 150 g (5½ oz) **turkey** stir fry strips
> 3 **spring onions**, sliced thinly
> ½ red or yellow **pepper**, de-seeded and
>   sliced thinly
> 1 small **carrot**, peeled and cut into thin strips
> 1 **celery stick**, sliced thinly
> 75 g (2¾ oz) **mushrooms**, sliced
> 50 g (1¾ oz) dried egg noodles
> salt and freshly ground black pepper

Method

1 Mix together the orange juice, soy sauce, chilli sauce and cornflour until smooth. Set to one side.

2 Heat a wok or large non stick frying pan and spray with the cooking spray. Add the turkey and stir fry briskly for 3–4 minutes. Add the spring onions, pepper, carrot, celery and mushrooms. Stir fry over a high heat for another 3–4 minutes, until the turkey is cooked. The vegetables should remain crisp.

3 Meanwhile, bring a pan of water to the boil. Add the noodles and cook according to the packet instructions. Drain thoroughly and set aside.

4 Stir the orange juice mixture, then add it to the stir fry and cook for a few moments until thickened. Add the noodles and toss together. Season to taste, then serve immediately.

Ⓥ **Try this...** For a vegetarian version, replace the **turkey** with 150 g (5½ oz) **Quorn Chicken Style Pieces** for the same *ProPoints* values.

Lamb and apricot curry

11 ProPoints value

❄ **Serves 4** ● **Takes 15** minutes to prepare,
1 hour to cook ● **44 ProPoints** values per recipe

low fat cooking spray
350 g (12 oz) lean lamb leg steaks, cut
    into chunks
2 tablespoons balti curry paste
1 large **onion**, chopped
600 ml (20 fl oz) lamb or vegetable stock
2 tablespoons tomato purée
1 red **pepper,** de-seeded and cut into chunks
100 g (3½ oz) **green beans**, trimmed and halved
200 g (7 oz) **cauliflower**, broken into florets
411 g can **apricot halves in natural juice**,
    drained and halved
50 g (1¾ oz) frozen **peas**
2 tablespoons chopped **fresh coriander**
150 g (5½ oz) dried long grain rice
1 tablespoon cornflour
4 tablespoons **low fat natural yogurt**

Method

1 Heat a large lidded saucepan and spray with the
cooking spray. Add the lamb, letting it sear and
brown before turning over. Cook for 3–4 minutes
until browned on all sides.
2 Add the curry paste, onion, stock and tomato
purée. Bring to the boil, then reduce the heat. Cover
and simmer for 40 minutes.
3 Add the pepper, green beans, cauliflower and
apricots to the curry. Simmer for 20 minutes, or until
the cauliflower is tender and then add the peas and
coriander.
4 Meanwhile, bring a pan of water to the boil and
cook the rice according to the packet instructions.
Drain thoroughly.
5 Blend the cornflour with 2 tablespoons of cold
water, add it to the curry and stir until thickened.
Cook for 1–2 minutes. Serve with the rice and a
tablespoon of yogurt each.

Vegetable jalfrezi

8 ProPoints value

Ⓥ ❄ **Serves 4** ● **Takes 20** minutes to prepare,
30 minutes to cook ● **33 ProPoints** values per recipe

low fat cooking spray
1 large **onion**, chopped
1 eating **apple**, unpeeled, cored and chopped
1 **garlic clove**, crushed
3 tablespoons jalfrezi curry paste
2 **carrots**, peeled and sliced
1 red **pepper**, de-seeded and chopped
400 g can chopped **tomatoes**
175 g (6 oz) **cauliflower** or **broccoli**, broken
    into florets
410 g can **chick peas**, drained
300 ml (10 fl oz) vegetable stock
50 g (1¾ oz) frozen **peas**
2 tablespoons chopped **fresh coriander**
salt and freshly ground black pepper

To serve
4 tablespoons **low fat plain yogurt**
4 plain Weight Watchers mini naan breads

Method

1 Heat a large lidded saucepan and spray with the
cooking spray. Add the onion, apple and garlic and
stir fry for 2 minutes. Add the curry paste and cook
for a few seconds more.
2 Add the carrots, pepper, tomatoes, cauliflower
or broccoli, chick peas and stock. Simmer, partially
covered, for 25–30 minutes, adding a little extra
stock or water if it seems to be getting too dry.
3 Add the peas and coriander and heat for a few
moments. Check the seasoning. Preheat the grill.
4 Warm the bread under the grill for a couple of
minutes. Serve the curry on warmed plates with
1 tablespoon of yogurt each and a naan bread.

Ⓥ **Try this...** Use 400 g (14 oz) **potatoes**, cut
into small chunks, instead of the **chick peas**,
for 9 **ProPoints** values per serving.

Spaghetti bolognese

❄ **Serves 4** ● **Takes 25** minutes to prepare,
30 minutes to cook ● **42 ProPoints** values per recipe

> 500 g (1 lb 2 oz) extra lean beef mince
> 1 large **onion**, chopped
> 2 **garlic cloves**, crushed
> 2 **celery sticks**, chopped
> 2 large **carrots**, peeled and chopped
> 300 ml (10 fl oz) beef or vegetable stock
> 400 g can chopped **tomatoes**
> 2 teaspoons Italian mixed dried herbs
> 2 tablespoons tomato purée
> 1 **courgette**, grated coarsely
> 200 g (7 oz) **mushrooms**, sliced
> 200 g (7 oz) dried spaghetti
> salt and freshly ground black pepper

Method

1 Heat a large, lidded, heavy based saucepan until hot. Add the beef mince, a handful at a time, and then let it sear over a high heat, stirring after 30–40 seconds. Cook for another 1–2 minutes until browned.

2 Add the onion, garlic, celery and carrots. Cook, stirring, for a further 2–3 minutes.

3 Pour in the stock, tip in the tomatoes and add the dried herbs, tomato purée, courgette and mushrooms. Stir well. Simmer, partially covered, for 25–30 minutes. Check the seasoning.

4 Bring a pan of water to the boil, add the pasta and cook for 10–12 minutes, or according to the packet instructions. Drain well, share between four warm plates and top with the meat sauce.

🅥 **Try this...** For a vegetarian version, use 500 g (1 lb 2 oz) **Quorn mince**, instead of beef, for 8 **ProPoints** values per serving. There's no need to brown the Quorn mince in step 1. Just add it to the saucepan in step 2, along with the **onion**, **garlic**, **celery** and **carrots**.

Chorizo lasagne

❄ **Serves 4** ● **Takes 40** minutes to prepare,
35 minutes to cook ● **27 ProPoints** values per recipe

> 400 g (14 oz) **butternut squash**, peeled,
>   de-seeded and cut into medium size chunks
> 1 red **onion**, cut into wedges
> 1 red **pepper**, de-seeded and cut into chunks
> 1 **courgette**, cut into chunks
> low fat cooking spray
> 50 g (1¾ oz) chorizo sausage, chopped
> 12 **cherry tomatoes**, halved
> 500 g jar tomato sauce for pasta
> 6 no need to precook, dried lasagne sheets
>   (about 120 g/4½ oz in total)
> 40 g pack Cheddar cheese sauce mix
> 300 ml (10 fl oz) **skimmed milk**
> salt and freshly ground black pepper

Method

1 Preheat the oven to Gas Mark 6/200°C/fan oven 180°C.

2 Put the squash, onion, pepper and courgette in a large roasting tin and spray with the cooking spray. Season and toss to coat. Roast for 15 minutes and then add the chorizo. Stir well, then roast for 5–10 more minutes, until the vegetables are tender.

3 Add the tomatoes to the vegetables and then stir in the tomato sauce.

4 Tip half of the vegetable mixture into a large rectangular baking dish, measuring about 25 x 20 cm (10 x 8 inches). Arrange three lasagne sheets on top. Repeat the layers.

5 Make the cheese sauce with the skimmed milk, following the packet instructions. Pour evenly over the top of the lasagne. Bake for 30–35 minutes, until golden brown. Remove from the oven and allow to stand for a few minutes, before serving.

Who doesn't **love** lasagne?

what's
for pudding?

Then you'll love these amazing sweet treats. You just can't beat **the flavours and aromas of home baking**, so you're sure to enjoy making favourites such as Queen of Puddings, Apricot Bread and Butter Pudding or Classic Rice Pudding again and again.

Pancakes with chocolate sauce

A pancake with chocolate sauce and ice cream is the ultimate pudding luxury.

Ⓨ ❋ **Serves 4** ● **Takes 20** minutes ● **30** *ProPoints* values per recipe

> 75 g (2¾ oz) plain flour
> a pinch of salt
> 1 **egg**
> 350 ml (12 fl oz) **skimmed milk**
> low fat cooking spray
> 25 g (1 oz) plain chocolate, broken into pieces
> 1 tablespoon golden syrup
> 2 tablespoons cocoa powder
> 2 teaspoons cornflour
> 4 x 60 g (2 oz) scoops low fat vanilla ice cream, to serve

Method

1 Sift the flour and salt into a large jug or mixing bowl. Add the egg and 200 ml (7 fl oz) of the milk. Beat with a hand whisk to make a smooth batter.

2 Heat a pancake pan or a non stick frying pan until hot and spray with the cooking spray. Pour in a thin stream of batter, tilting the pan so that it evenly covers the surface. Cook over a medium heat until the surface has set, then flip the pancake over to cook the other side. Make four pancakes in total, spraying the pan with the cooking spray before cooking each one. Keep the pancakes in a warm place until all of them are cooked.

3 To make the sauce, put the chocolate, golden syrup, cocoa powder, cornflour and remaining milk in a non stick saucepan. Heat gently over a low heat, stirring constantly with a small whisk or wooden spoon until thickened, smooth and glossy.

4 Put each pancake on a warm serving plate and add one scoop of ice cream to each. Pour an equal amount of chocolate sauce over each one and serve.

Classic rice pudding

4 ProPoints value

Why not top this lovely dessert with some tart low calorie jam, such as apricot or blackcurrant? Add 2 heaped teaspoons per person for an additional 1 *ProPoints* value per serving.

Ⓥ **Serves 4** ● **Takes 10** minutes to prepare, **1¼** hours to bake ● **18** *ProPoints* values per recipe

> *50 g (1¾ oz) short grain pudding rice, rinsed*
> *25 g (1 oz) light muscovado sugar*
> *600 ml (20 fl oz) skimmed milk*
> *170 g can light evaporated milk*
> *½ teaspoon vanilla extract*
> *a good pinch of freshly grated or ground nutmeg*

Method

1 Preheat the oven to Gas Mark 3/160°C/fan oven 140°C.

2 Put the rice into a 850 ml (1½ pint) deep ovenproof dish. Add the sugar, milk, evaporated milk, vanilla extract and nutmeg. Stir to dissolve the sugar. If you wish, sprinkle a little extra nutmeg over the surface.

3 Bake the pudding in the centre of the oven for 1¼ hours. Cool for a few moments then serve.

Tips... The evaporated milk and muscovado sugar give a delicious, caramelised flavour but it's possible to use caster sugar instead of muscovado. The *ProPoints* values will remain the same.

... The ideal time to bake this dish is when you're cooking a casserole in the oven, to make full use of the oven space.

> *Cook's ideas...*
> **Check if your eggs are fresh.** A fresh egg feels heavy in the hand and sinks in a bowl of water while an older one floats vertically.

Queen of puddings

7 ProPoints value

Ⓥ **Serves 4** ● **Takes 10** minutes to prepare + **15** minutes soaking, **30** minutes to bake
● **28** *ProPoints* values per recipe

> *2 teaspoons low fat spread*
> *100 g (3½ oz) fresh white breadcrumbs*
> *450 ml (16 fl oz) skimmed milk*
> *1 teaspoon vanilla extract*
> *80 g (3 oz) caster sugar*
> *4 eggs, separated*
> *2 tablespoons low calorie raspberry jam*

Method

1 Grease a 1 litre (1¾ pint) baking dish with 1 teaspoon of the low fat spread. Sprinkle the breadcrumbs into the baking dish.

2 Heat the milk, remaining low fat spread and vanilla extract until just lukewarm – take care that the mixture doesn't get too hot. Remove from the heat and add 50 g (1¾ oz) of the sugar. Beat in the egg yolks. Pour into the baking dish and stir into the breadcrumbs, then leave to soak for 15 minutes. Meanwhile, preheat the oven to Gas Mark 4/180°C/fan oven 160°C.

3 Bake the pudding for 20–25 minutes, until set. Remove the baking dish from the oven, cool for 5 minutes, then spread the jam over the surface.

4 Whisk the egg whites in a clean, grease-free bowl until they hold their shape, then add the remaining sugar, whisking again until stiff and glossy. Pile the meringue on top of the pudding, then return it to the oven to bake for a further 5–8 minutes, until golden brown. Serve at once.

Ⓥ **Try this...** Replace the raspberry jam with strawberry, blackcurrant or apricot low calorie jam. They are all equally delicious in this recipe and the *ProPoints* values will remain the same.

Tip... To make this recipe serve 2, simply halve the quantities. The *ProPoints* values per serving remain the same.

This classic pudding is **heavenly**

Raspberry and toasted oat treat

This simple recipe is inspired by the traditional Scottish recipe, Atholl Brose, but our version has no cream or alcohol.

Y **Serves 1** ● **Takes 10** minutes ● **4** *ProPoints* values per recipe

> 15 g (½ oz) **porridge oats**
> 40 g (1½ oz) low fat soft cheese
> 2 tablespoons **low fat natural yogurt**
> 1 teaspoon caster sugar
> a few drops of vanilla extract
> 75 g (2¾ oz) frozen **raspberries**, thawed

Method

1 Preheat the grill to high. Sprinkle the porridge oats on to a baking sheet and toast them lightly, taking care that they don't burn. Leave to cool.
2 Beat the soft cheese in a mixing bowl until smooth, then mix in the yogurt, sugar and vanilla extract. Stir in the cooled oats.
3 Spoon half of the raspberries into a serving glass. Stir the rest through the soft cheese mixture, though it's nice if they are only partially stirred through to give an attractive swirled effect. Spoon into the glass and then chill until ready to serve.

Tip... To thaw frozen **raspberries** quickly, microwave them on high for 40 seconds. Don't worry if they are a bit mushy.

Rhubarb and custard fool

Quick and creamy, this is an ideal dessert for one.

Y **Serves 1** ● **Takes 15** minutes to prepare + chilling ● **4** *ProPoints* values per recipe

> 125 g (4½ oz) **rhubarb**, trimmed and sliced into short pieces
> 2 tablespoons artificial sweetener
> 50 g (1¾ oz) low fat custard
> 50 g (1¾ oz) half fat crème fraîche

Method

1 Put the rhubarb in a small saucepan with 3 tablespoons of water and the sweetener. Heat and simmer gently for 6–8 minutes until tender. Take care that the saucepan doesn't boil dry. Add an extra 1–2 tablespoons of water, if needed.
2 Tip the rhubarb into a bowl so that it cools quickly, then drain off any excess liquid through a strainer (there should only be a little).
3 Mix together the custard and crème fraîche, then fold through the cooled rhubarb. Spoon into a glass, then cover and chill until ready to serve.

Y **Try this...** You could use **0% fat Greek yogurt** instead of crème fraîche. The ***ProPoints*** values per serving will be 2.

Y **Or this...** Instead of **rhubarb**, use **gooseberries** when they are in season. The ***ProPoints*** values per serving will remain the same.

Cook's ideas...
Enjoy fruit in season – and then freeze any you don't need. It will still taste great the next time since frozen fruit retains all of its flavour.

Plum, apple and almond crumble

Muscovado sugar makes this fruity crumble especially delicious.

Ⓥ ❄ **Serves 4** ● **Takes 15** minutes to prepare, **35** minutes to bake ● **18** *ProPoints* values per recipe

4 **plums**, pitted and sliced

300 g (10½ oz) cooking **apples**, peeled, cored and sliced

25 g (1 oz) sultanas

1 tablespoon lemon juice

40 g (1½ oz) light muscovado sugar

¼ teaspoon ground cinnamon (optional)

50 g (1¾ oz) plain flour

25 g (1 oz) **porridge oats**

a pinch of salt

20 g (¾ oz) low fat spread

15 g (½ oz) flaked almonds

Method

1 Preheat the oven to Gas Mark 4/180°C/fan oven 160°C.

2 Put the plums, apples and sultanas into a 1.2 litre (2 pint) deep baking dish. Add the lemon juice, 1 tablespoon of water, 25 g (1 oz) of the sugar and the cinnamon (if using). Stir to mix. Bake for 10 minutes.

3 Meanwhile, put the flour, porridge oats and salt into a mixing bowl and add the low fat spread. Rub it in with your fingertips until the mixture resembles breadcrumbs, then stir in the almonds and the rest of the sugar.

4 Remove the baking dish from the oven and sprinkle the topping evenly over the fruit. Return the dish to the oven and bake for 30–35 minutes until golden brown. Serve immediately.

Banana and ginger puddings

7 ProPoints value

Ⓥ ❄ **Serves 4 ● Takes 15** minutes to prepare,
25 minutes to cook ● **27** *ProPoints* values per recipe

> *40 g (1½ oz) low fat spread*
> *15 g (½ oz) stem ginger in syrup, sliced thinly,
>   plus 4 teaspoons syrup from the jar*
> *40 g (1½ oz) light muscovado sugar*
> *75 g (2¾ oz) self raising flour*
> *¼ teaspoon ground ginger*
> *1 tablespoon* **skimmed milk**
> *¼ teaspoon vanilla extract*
> *1* **egg**
> *1* **banana***, mashed*
> *a kettleful of boiling water*
> *150 g pot hot or cold low fat custard, to serve*

Method

1 Use a tiny amount of the low fat spread to grease four individual 6 cm (2½ inch) pudding basins. Alternatively, use ramekins. Share the stem ginger between them, adding 1 teaspoon of the syrup to each.
2 Put the remaining low fat spread into a mixing bowl with the sugar, flour, ginger, milk and vanilla extract. Add the egg, then beat with a wooden spoon for 1 minute, until all the ingredients are combined. Mix in the banana.
3 Share the mixture between the four prepared basins, then place a piece of foil on top of each one, wrapping it tightly around.
4 Place the basin in a large lidded saucepan and add enough boiling water to come about one third of the way up the sides of the basins. Put the lid on and steam over a low heat for 25 minutes. Check the water level to make sure it doesn't boil dry. Top up with extra boiling water, if needed.
5 Run a knife around the pudding basins and invert to release them. Serve each one with an equal amount of hot or cold custard.

Apricot bread and butter pudding

5 ProPoints value

Add some creaminess with 2 tablespoons of low fat plain yogurt per person for an extra 1 *ProPoints* value per serving.

Ⓥ **Serves 4 ● Takes 10** minutes to prepare
+ 20 minutes soaking, **35** minutes to bake
● **22** *ProPoints* values per recipe

> *25 g (1 oz) low fat spread*
> *4 low calorie, slightly stale, white bread slices*
> *50 g (1¾ oz) ready to eat, semi-dried apricots,
>   chopped*
> *25 g (1 oz) sultanas or raisins*
> *2* **eggs**
> *450 ml (16 fl oz)* **skimmed milk**
> *1 teaspoon vanilla extract*
> *20 g (¾ oz) caster sugar*

Method

1 Grease a 1.2 litre (2 pint) baking dish with a small amount of the low fat spread then spread the rest of it on to the bread slices. Cut each slice into four triangles. Arrange them in the dish with the chopped apricots and sultanas or raisins.
2 Beat together the eggs, milk and vanilla extract. Stir in the sugar, allowing a few minutes for it to dissolve. Pour the mixture over the bread and fruit. Cover with cling film and leave to soak for at least 20 minutes. Preheat the oven to Gas Mark 4/180°C/ fan oven 160°C.
3 Remove the cling film from the pudding and bake for about 30–35 minutes until set and golden brown. Serve immediately.

Ⓥ **Try this...** For a lovely festive twist, soak the apricots and sultanas or raisins in 25 ml (1 fl oz) rum or brandy overnight and then add the soaked fruit and brandy in step 1, following the recipe. The *ProPoints* values per serving will be 6.

Treat yourself to something **yummy**

Egg custards with cherries

Serves 2 ● **Takes 10** minutes to prepare,
25 minutes to bake + **20** minutes cooling
● **10** *ProPoints* values per recipe

> 40 g (1½ oz) dried sour cherries
> 300 ml (10 fl oz) **skimmed milk**
> ¼ teaspoon vanilla extract
> 15 g (½ oz) caster sugar
> 1 **egg**, beaten

Method

1 Preheat the oven to Gas Mark 4/180°C/fan oven 160°C. Put the cherries in a small saucepan with 5 tablespoons of cold water. Bring up to the boil, then simmer gently for 8–10 minutes, or until the liquid has just evaporated, ensuring they don't boil dry. Share them between two ramekin dishes or individual baking dishes.
2 Warm the milk in the same saucepan until just lukewarm. Remove from the heat. Add the vanilla extract and sugar, stirring to dissolve.
3 Take care that the milk isn't too hot (otherwise it could scramble) and then beat in the egg. Strain through a sieve into the baking dishes.
4 Stand the dishes in a deep baking dish or roasting tin and pour some warm water around them to come about one third of the way up the sides. Bake for 25 minutes until set. Cool for about 20 minutes before serving.

Tip... In step 4, standing the dishes in a baking dish with warm water (called a bain marie) helps to create an even temperature which gives a smoother set to the custards.

Try this... Instead of dried cherries, use 75 g (2¾ oz) pitted **fresh cherries** for 3 *ProPoints* values per serving.

Blackberry and apple trifles

At the end of summer, pick a few blackberries from the hedges to enjoy in this dessert.

Serves 2 ● **Takes 20** minutes ● **7** *ProPoints* values per recipe

> 75 g (2¾ oz) **blackberries**
> 1 eating **apple**, such as Cox, peeled,
>   cored and sliced thinly
> 1 tablespoon caster sugar
> 3 sponge fingers
> 75 g (2¾ oz) low fat soft cheese
> 2 tablespoons **low fat plain yogurt**
> ½ teaspoon finely grated orange or lemon zest
> 1 teaspoon orange or lemon juice
> a few orange or lemon slices, to decorate

Method

1 Reserve a few blackberries for decoration then put the remainder in a small saucepan with the apple, 2 teaspoons of sugar and 5 tablespoons of cold water. Simmer for 10 minutes, stirring occasionally, until the apple is cooked. Remove from the heat.
2 Break the sponge fingers in half and place three pieces in the base of two serving glasses. Share the apple and blackberries between the glasses, adding any juice, which will be soaked up by the sponge fingers.
3 Beat together the soft cheese, yogurt, orange or lemon zest, juice and the remaining 1 teaspoon of sugar until smooth. Spoon on top of the desserts, then cover and chill until ready to eat.
4 Serve decorated with orange or lemon slices and the reserved blackberries.

Try this... When **blackberries** are out of season, use frozen ones instead, or substitute frozen **forest fruits**. The *ProPoints* values per serving will remain the same.

Mini Christmas puddings

Ⓥ **Serves 6** ● **Takes 20** minutes + overnight soaking, **1½** hours to steam + **45** minutes reheating
● **32** *ProPoints* values per recipe

75 g (2¾ oz) seedless raisins

75 g (2¾ oz) currants

25 g (1 oz) dried cranberries

25 g (1 oz) glacé cherries, chopped

½ a kettleful of boiling water

100 ml (3½ fl oz) unsweetened apple juice

2 tablespoons brandy

100 g (3½ oz) fresh white breadcrumbs

1 **carrot**, peeled and grated finely

1 teaspoon finely grated orange zest

40 g (1½ oz) dark muscovado sugar

1 teaspoon ground mixed spice

1 **egg**, beaten

1 teaspoon low fat spread

Method

1 Put the raisins, currants, cranberries and cherries in a mixing bowl. Pour over enough boiling water to cover them, then leave for 10 minutes. Drain thoroughly. This helps to plump up the fruit and makes the puddings really moist.

2 Add the apple juice and brandy to the fruit, stir well, then cover and leave overnight in the fridge.

3 The next day, add the breadcrumbs, carrot, orange zest, sugar, mixed spice and egg to the fruit. Stir thoroughly to mix well.

4 Use the low fat spread to grease four individual 6 cm (2½ inch) pudding basins. Spoon an equal amount of mixture into each one. Level the tops, then cover tightly with pieces of foil.

5 Put the puddings in a steamer over gently simmering water and steam for 1½ hours, topping up the steamer with boiling water, as necessary.

6 Cool the puddings and replace the pieces of foil with fresh pieces, or wrap in greaseproof paper. On Christmas Day, reheat the puddings in the steamer for a further 45 minutes.

Tip... If you don't have a steamer, put the basins in a large saucepan with a tight fitting lid. Add enough boiling water to come one third of the way up the sides of the basins. Cover and cook for 1½ hours, topping up with boiling water as necessary, and follow step 6.

ProPoints values index

Wake up call

4 ProPoints values and under

Eggy bread with bananas 8

Scotch pancakes with turkey rashers 10

5 ProPoints values and under

Carrot cake muffins 12

Courgette and chorizo frittata 11

Creamy mushrooms on toast 14

Spiced fruits with cinnamon toast 7

Strawberry muesli smoothie 12

6 ProPoints values and under

Porridge with mango and pineapple 8

Rosti with sausages and eggs 14

Smoked fish ramekins 15

Lunch break

2 ProPoints values and under

Butternut squash pâté 19

Creamy broccoli and spinach soup 24

3 ProPoints values and under

Carrot and red lentil soup 26

Crunchy coleslaw with pine nut kernels 18

4 ProPoints values and under

Chunky butter bean soup 17

5 ProPoints values and under

Cullen skink 26

Curried chicken soup 20

Leek and ham gratins 28

6 ProPoints values and under

Bubble and squeak 28

Pasta with peppers and courgettes 18

7 ProPoints values and under

New potato and tuna salad 24

8 ProPoints values and under

Cheddar sandwich with beetroot slaw 23

Egg and cress bagel 22

Fruity chicken and rice salad 27

Jubilee chicken sandwich 20

9 ProPoints values and under

Salmon and cucumber wrap 22

Traditional suppers

5 ProPoints values and under

Chicken in red wine 32

6 ProPoints values and under

Good shepherd's pie 37

Toad in the hole 33

7 ProPoints values and under

Lamb and barley stew 36

8 ProPoints values and under

Filo turkey pie 31

Lancashire lobscouse 32

Steak and mushroom pies 38

9 ProPoints values and under

Bacon and onion hotpot 38

11 ProPoints values and under

Rosti fish pie 34

Smoked pollock kedgeree 39

14 ProPoints values and under

Baked fish and spicy chips 34

Modern suppers

6 ProPoints values and under

Sausages with peppers and lentils 44

7 ProPoints values and under

Chorizo lasagne 50

8 ProPoints values and under

Cottage pie with potato thatch 46

Vegetable jalfrezi 48

9 ProPoints values and under

Chilli con carne 42

10 ProPoints values and under

Tuna and sweetcorn fish cakes 44

11 ProPoints values and under

Lamb and apricot curry 48

Spaghetti bolognese 50

12 ProPoints values and under

Turkey stir fry 47

13 ProPoints values and under

Chicken korma 42

Macaroni cheese with leeks 46

Seared salmon and horseradish mash 41

What's for pudding?

3 ProPoints values and under

Blackberry and apple trifles 60

4 ProPoints values and under

Classic rice pudding 54

Raspberry and toasted oat treat 56

Rhubarb and custard fool 56

5 ProPoints values and under

Apricot bread and butter pudding 58

Egg custards with cherries 60

Mini Christmas puddings 61

Plum, apple and almond crumble 57

7 ProPoints values and under

Banana and ginger puddings 58

Queen of puddings 54

8 ProPoints values and under

Pancakes with chocolate sauce 53